Mom
Share Your Life With Me

Created by Kathleen Lashier

Copyright © 2012 Linkages

To contact the author:

Linkages Memory Journals • P.O. Box 8282 • Des Moines, IA 50301
888-815-9063
www.mymemoryjournals.com

Printed in the U.S.A.
by G&R Publishing Co.

ISBN-13: 978-1-56383-415-8
ISBN-10: 1-56383-415-4

Distributed by:

CQ Products
507 Industrial Street • Waverly, IA 50677
800-887-4445 • Fax 800-886-7496

Name all the street addresses you can recall and/or all the communities you've lived in and years there.

January 10

January 11

What did your father do for a living?

January 12

*Did your mother work
outside the home?*

_____

_____

_____

_____

_____

_____

_____

_____

January 13

*Tell a nickname your
family gave you and
how you got it.*

_____

_____

_____

_____

_____

_____

_____

_____

January 14

*Tell of any other nicknames
in your family.* _____

_____

_____

_____

_____

_____

_____

_____

_____

_____

_____

January 15

*Tell a fond memory
of your Grandpa.* _____

_____

_____

_____

_____

_____

_____

_____

_____

_____

_____

January 16

*Tell a fond memory
of your Grandma.*

January 17

Tell about a favorite Aunt.

January 18

Tell about a favorite Uncle.

January 19

*Relate an experience or
memory of a cousin.*

January 20

*Did any relatives ever
live with you? If not, then
relate another memory of
cousins, aunts or uncles.*

January 21

When it was time for discipline, which parent corrected you and how?

Tell about the naughtiest thing you ever did. If you got caught, describe the consequences.

Who was the President
when you were born?
_____
_____
_____

At what age did you first vote
and for whom did you cast
your first Presidential vote?
_____
_____
_____

Did you ever see a President
or Vice-President in person?
_____
_____

Which of the Presidents in your lifetime
has been your favorite and why?
_____
_____
_____
_____
_____

Did you ever have an imaginary friend?

What did you and your brothers or sisters fight about the most?

Tell about an experience or
event that drew you together.

January 29

Tell about the worst winter storm
that you can remember as a child.

January 30

What did you use to go sledding
down a hill in the snow?

January 31

*What extras did you use for your snowman's
face, buttons, arms, hat, etc?* _____

_____

_____

_____

_____

_____

_____

February 1

*Do you have any ice skating
memories to share?* _____

_____

_____

_____

_____

_____

February 2

*Share a memory about a weather-
related school cancellation.* _____

_____

_____

_____

_____

February 3

*Do you have any knowledge of
the origins of your family name?*

*How did you first
smash a finger?*

Who was the most famous
person you ever met as a child?

Tell about someone who had
a big influence on your life.

Tell about another
influential person in your life.

Tell about a big lie you told.

What was your favorite
meal as a child?

Who was your first
boyfriend?

Tell about the Valentine
Day festivities at your school.

*Tell about a special
valentine you once gave.*

February 13

*Tell about a special valentine
you once received.*

February 14

Tell about your first date.

Tell about your first kiss.

*Tell about your first
favorite TV shows.*

February 15

February 16

February 17

Tell about family reunions
in your childhood.

What do you remember as
your favorite subject in school?

What do your remember as your least favorite school subject?

What is the biggest problem you remember having in Grade School?

What is the biggest problem you
remember having in Jr. High school?

_____

_____

_____

_____

_____

February 22

What is the biggest problem you
remember having in Sr. High school?

_____

_____

_____

_____

February 23

Tell about a great victory or personal
success story from your school days.

_____

_____

_____

_____

February 24

Did you and your friends ever have a secret hide-out?

February 25

Tell about a favorite restaurant or public place where you and your friends liked to gather.

February 26

*Tell about the best
pet you ever had.*

*Tell about other
pets you had.*

Tell about being in a
school play or program.

Tell about a school
principal you remember.

Did you ever pretend to be sick as an
excuse to stay home from school?

March 3

Did you ever get in trouble
for saying a bad word?

March 4

Tell about how you spent your
Saturdays during the school year.

March 5

Tell about how you
spent your Sundays.

March 6

What was the naughtiest or meanest
thing you remember doing in school?
Were there consequences?

March 7

When on car trips, did
you play car games?

March 8

Tell of a difficult essay or
term paper assignment.

What radio programs or
stations were your favorites?

What was the first movie you
ever saw and who starred in it?

March 11

What was your favorite
movie and why?

March 12

*Did kids ever tease
you and why?*

March 13

*Do you remember
your first pizza?*

March 14

If you went to college, tell which college you chose and why. _____

_____

_____

_____

_____

_____

March 15

Tell your major and how you chose it. _____

_____

_____

_____

_____

_____

March 16

Tell me more about your college years, or your work experiences in early adulthood. _____

_____

_____

_____

_____

March 17

What do you remember as
your favorite time of year? Why? _____

_____

_____

_____

_____

_____

_____

_____

_____

March 18

Describe some household
chores you had as a child. _____

_____

_____

_____

_____

_____

_____

_____

March 19

*Describe some
outside chores.*

*Which chore did you dislike the most
and how did you try to get out of it?*

Did you have a favorite chore?

What bones have you
broken and how?

Did you ever
need stitches?

Do you have any other good
stories about being injured?

Tell of a childhood illness.

March 25

*Tell about an experience at
the doctor's or dentist's office.*

March 26

What memories do you have of
St. Patrick's Day in your childhood?

March 27

If you ever hitch-hiked, explain.

March 28

*Name your best
school friends.*

*Tell of a nickname given to you by
friends or classmates. How did you
get it? How did you feel about it?*

March 29

March 30

*What were some crazy names
or nicknames in your school?* _____

_____

_____

_____

_____

_____

March 31

*Do you have a good
April Fool's Day story?* _____

_____

_____

_____

_____

_____

April 1

*Tell about a practical joke or
prank you played on someone.* _____

_____

_____

_____

_____

_____

April 2

Tell about a practical joke or
prank someone played on you? _____

_____

_____

_____

_____

_____

_____

_____

_____

April 3

Did you ever make a kite?
How? Tell about your _____
kite-flying experiences. _____

_____

_____

_____

_____

_____

_____

_____

_____

April 4

Did you ever feel a hatred for another person? Explain.

April 5

As a child, what did you want to be when you grew up?

April 6

Did you ever bring home or try to adopt a wild animal?

April 7

Relate a favorite spring memory.

April 8

Did your Mom or Dad ever find something you had hidden?

April 9

Make up a limerick about yourself.
There once was a… _____

_____

_____

_____

_____

_____

_____

_____

_____

_____

Now make up a limerick about me.
There once was a… _____

_____

_____

_____

_____

_____

_____

_____

_____

Share a memory of going to
church as you were growing up.

April 12

Share a memory about a
church social activity.

April 13

*(If the following Easter topics do not apply, please share
your special Holiday memories and traditions.)*

Tell about an Easter Egg hunt.

April 14

*Tell about any other
Easter traditions.*

April 15

*Did you ever have a
recurring dream as a child?*

April 16

*When you played make-
believe, what did you pretend?*

April 17

Tell about the best birthday
present you ever received.

_____

_____

_____

_____

_____

_____

April 18

Tell about any sports you
played in Jr. or Sr. High.

_____

_____

_____

_____

_____

April 19

Did you ever write something
that you were really proud of?

_____

_____

_____

_____

_____

April 20

*What was your favorite
book as a youth?*

*What is the biggest
physical problem you
had to deal with?*

*Did you have
any superstitions?*

April 23

*Where were your best
hide-and-seek places?*

April 24

*Tell about the first time you were
ever behind the wheel of a car.*

April 25

Did you ever take anything
that wasn't yours? _____

_____

_____

_____

_____

_____

_____

_____

_____

April 26

What did you do with it?
Did you get caught? _____

_____

_____

_____

_____

_____

_____

_____

April 27

*Do you have a story
about a big surprise?*

April 28

*What childhood fear
do you remember?*

April 29

How much do you remember
paying for an ice cream cone?

April 30

Tell about a
May Day tradition.

May 1

What were May Baskets made
of and what did they contain?

May 2

*Did you have
a treehouse?*

*Were you ever
bitten by a dog?*

Did your mother ever
make a special gift for you?

May 5

Tell a favorite memory
of your mother.

May 6

Tell about some good advice
your mother gave you.

May 7

Relate your family Mother's Day traditions, or tell me
more about what kind of person your mother was.

May 8

Do you remember any
childhood songs or rhymes? _____

_____

_____

_____

_____

_____

_____

_____

_____

May 9

Name some popular hit
songs from your youth. _____

_____

_____

_____

_____

_____

_____

_____

_____

May 10

What was your favorite
singing group or band? _____

_____

_____

_____

_____

_____

May 11

Tell a favorite singer and
a song that he/she sang? _____

_____

_____

_____

_____

May 12

What kind of dances
did you do as a youth? _____

_____

_____

_____

_____

May 13

*Tell about the first
dance you ever went to.*

*Tell about your high school
prom or formal dance.*

Describe your military experience
or that of someone in your family.

May 16

Share a memory involving a war
during your childhood or youth.

May 17

Share another memory involving
a war during childhood or youth.

May 18

If you have another photograph of
your childhood to share, place it here.

May 19

*Tell about your graduation
exercises or traditions.*

May 20

*What year did you graduate from high school?
What do you recall about your feelings, emotions,
hopes and dreams at this time of your life?*

May 21

*How many students were in your high
school? In your graduating class?*

May 22

*Did you have homework
during your school years?*

*Tell of someone you
envied and why.*

Describe a very proud
moment in your childhood.

May 25

Tell about Memorial Day
traditions during your youth.

May 26

Share a special memory
of Memorial Day.

May 27

Did you play a
musical instrument?

May 28

Tell about the closest friend
you had during your childhood.

May 29

Is there anything you have now that you have kept from your childhood?

_____

_____

_____

_____

_____

_____

_____

_____

_____

_____

May 30

Do you have any good bathtime stories?

_____

_____

_____

_____

_____

_____

_____

_____

_____

May 31

*Tell about a strange person
that lived in your town.*

June 1

*Describe a place you
liked to go to be alone.*

June 2

*Did you ever sleep
under the stars?*

*Tell about hot dog or
marshmallow roasting.*

Did you ever go on a
camp out? Tell about it.

June 5

Did you ever go
on a snipe hunt?

June 6

Do you remember a favorite
snack that you liked to make?

June 7

Share a horse-riding story.

June 8

What was your first job?
How much did you get paid?

June 9

*Tell about other paying
jobs you had as a youth.*

*What was your first purchase
using your own money?*

If you were ever in
a parade, tell about it.

June 12

Tell another memory
about a parade.

June 13

Share a childhood memory
about a death that affected you.

June 14

Relate your happiest
memory as a youth.

June 15

How did you learn to swim?

June 16

Where did you go to swim and
what kind of suits did you wear?

June 17

Tell a favorite memory
of your father.

_____

_____

_____

_____

_____

_____

_____

_____

_____

_____

_____

June 18

Tell about some good
advice your father gave you.

_____

_____

_____

_____

_____

_____

_____

_____

June 19

Relate your family Father's Day traditions, or tell me more about what kind of person your father was.

June 20

Did your father ever make a special gift for you?

June 21

*Did you have a special nature
place where you went to explore?*

June 22

*Did you ever go
skinny-dipping?*

June 23

*Did you ever
make mud pies?*

*Did you go barefoot in the
summer? If so, relate an experience
about stepping on something.*

*Describe a few of the favorite
hair styles of your youth.*

June 26

Tell about a bike you had.

June 27

*Tell about your
first very own car.*

June 28

*Did you ever have
or make a swing?*

June 29

*Tell about seeing something you
thought was very beautiful.*

June 30

*Describe an outside
game you made up.*

July 1

*Describe an inside
game you made up.*

*What kind of fireworks did people
have when you were a youth?*

Tell about Independence Day traditions of your childhood.

_____
_____
_____
_____
_____
_____
_____
_____
_____

July 4

Do you have a special July 4th that you remember most?

_____
_____
_____
_____
_____
_____
_____
_____
_____

July 5

Did you ever go to carnivals or amusement parks? Where?

_____
_____
_____
_____
_____
_____

July 6

What kinds of rides and games were there? How much did they cost?

_____
_____
_____
_____
_____

July 7

Tell about any State Fair or County Fair experiences.

_____
_____
_____
_____
_____

July 8

Tell about going to a circus, a
Chautauqua, or a hometown
celebration/festival.

July 9

Tell any favorite
summertime memory.

July 10

Did you go fishing, hunting or trapping in your youth?

_____

_____

_____

_____

_____

_____

_____

_____

_____

July 11

Tell about your biggest or best catch.

_____

_____

_____

_____

_____

_____

_____

_____

July 12

Do you remember having a favorite
candy? How much did it cost? _____

_____

_____

_____

_____

_____

July 13

Tell about the first meal you
ever made by yourself. _____

_____

_____

_____

July 14

Share a memory about
going on a picnic. _____

_____

_____

_____

_____

July 15

What kinds of party games or
party activities were popular?

July 16

Share a memory involving
a heatwave or drought.

July 17

*What did you
do to stay cool?*

July 18

*What was your favorite
holiday of the year? Why?*

July 19

*Share a birthday
party memory.*

_____

_____

_____

_____

_____

_____

_____

July 20

*Tell about the neatest shoes
you ever owned as a youth.*

_____

_____

_____

_____

_____

_____

July 21

*Share a memory
about a power outage.*

*Relate a memory involving
a flood or cloudburst.*

*Relate a memory of a tornado,
hurricane, or destructive wind.*

July 22

July 23

July 24

*What memories do you
have of lightning or thunder
during your childhood?*

July 25

*Share a special memory
about riding in a boat.*

July 26

Tell about a family
vacation trip.

July 27

Share the best vacation
experience you can recall.

July 28

Share the most unpleasant
vacation experience you can recall.

July 29

Do you have any other
 memories about a river,
lake, or beach to share?

July 30

Tell a memory about riding
on a ferry, bus, train, or plane.

July 31

If you were to return to your youth,
what would you do differently?

Describe your childhood
home & neighborhood.

Tell about going to
a summer camp.

August 3

Tell of an experience climbing
a mountain or big hill.

August 4

*Tell a memory about having company
at your house, or of a family party.*

*Tell about board games and card
games you played as a youth.*

Did your mom or dad have
a favorite remedy for when
you were sick or hurt?

August 7

Share an experience about
poison ivy or poison weed,
a bee sting or bug bite.

August 8

What was your best talent?

August 9

Tell about a time
when you got lost.

_____

_____

_____

_____

_____

_____

_____

_____

_____

_____

August 10

Did you ever play in
the sprinkler or hose?

_____

_____

_____

_____

_____

_____

_____

_____

August 11

*What was the dumbest stunt ever
pulled by you and a brother or sister?* _____

_____

_____

Were there consequences? _____

_____

_____

_____

_____

_____

August 12

*Did you have any favorite family
songs that you sang together?* _____

_____

_____

_____

_____

_____

_____

_____

August 13

Tell about your bedroom. _____

_____

_____

_____

_____

_____

*Share a memory of staying
overnight with a friend.* _____

_____

_____

_____

_____

*If you ever ran away
from home, tell about it.* _____

_____

_____

_____

_____

Do you remember being really
curious about something? _____

_____

_____

_____

_____

_____

_____

_____

_____

Share your childhood
experiences with roller skates. _____

_____

_____

_____

_____

_____

_____

_____

_____

_____

Did you ever experience home sickness?

Did you ever make a purchase that you later regretted?

Share an early experience
with make-up.

August 21

Tell about a favorite doll,
teddy bear, or other stuffed toy.

August 22

What other toys did
you like to play with?

August 23

Did you have to abide by
a curfew as a youth?

If you ever had a hero,
tell who. Tell why.

Phones have changed over the years. Describe how you used a phone to call up a childhood friend.

Did you ever have a fire in your home or accidentally catch something on fire?

*Tell about going to box
socials or pot lucks.*

_____

_____

_____

_____

_____

_____

_____

August 28

*Tell about an incident
when you were very angry
with your mom or dad.*

_____

_____

_____

_____

_____

_____

_____

August 29

Tell about an incident when your
mom or dad was very angry with you.

August 30

Share a memory
involving an outhouse.

August 31

Do you remember any Labor
Day traditions of your youth?

September 1

VJ Day...Do you have a memory
involving the end of World War II?
If not, then share a memory of Vietnam.

September 2

Back-To-School-Days...
What do you remember about that
big yearly "First Day of School"?

September 3

*Tell about your school
year calendar.* _____

_____

_____

_____

_____

_____

_____

_____

_____

_____

September 4

Tell about a school bully. _____

_____

_____

_____

_____

_____

_____

_____

_____

September 5

*What do you remember
doing at recess?*

*Tell about the playground
equipment at your grade school.*

*Did your parents ever make you
wear something stupid to school?*

Tell about who you thought was
the smartest kid in school and why.

Tell about the naughtiest
kid in school.

September 9

September 10

How did you experience
the 9/11 attacks?

September 11

September 12

Name the schools
that you went to.

What was your most
embarrassing school moment?

What teacher did you
dislike the most? Why?

Describe a typical school
day outfit in grade school… _____

_____

In high school… _____

_____

Where did you usually
buy your clothes? _____

_____

September 16

If you were ever in
a fight, tell about it. _____

_____

_____

_____

_____

_____

_____

September 17

*Did you ever have a
crush on a teacher?*

September 18

*Who was the best teacher
you ever had? Why?*

September 19

*What did your report cards
usually have to say about you?*

September 20

*What is the worst trick that
you remember a student
playing on a teacher?*

_____

*What is the meanest thing that you
remember a teacher doing to a student!*

_____

*How did you get to
and from school?*

*Do you remember a special
school custodian?*

What were your school colors?

*What was your
school mascot?*

September 26

*Tell about a memorable
birthday cake.*

September 27

Did you ever have a "good friend"
who did something mean to you?

September 28

How did your school
observe Homecoming?

September 29

Do you have any special Homecoming experiences to relate?

September 30

Did your High School have cheerleaders? What did they wear?

October 1

Can you recite any of your school cheers?

October 2

Tell about any other
extra-curricular activities.

October 3

Do you have a memory of
going to a big concert?

October 4

Do you have any special memories
about raking and burning leaves,
or mowing the lawn?

October 5

If you ever played in
the leaves, tell about it.

October 6

Do you have some
good advice for me?

October 7

October 8

What was your most prized possession as a child?

October 9

Share a memory about a bat in the house.

October 10

Relate a story about a mouse in the house.

October 11

What allowance did you get at different ages during your youth?

October 12

Did you have to do anything to earn it?

October 13

Do you have any advice on how
to be wise with my money? _____

_____

_____

_____

_____

_____

_____

_____

_____

_____

October 14

What is the strangest thing
you ever saw in the sky? _____

_____

_____

_____

_____

_____

_____

_____

_____

October 15

*Tell about pulling
or losing a baby tooth.*

*Did you ever lose something
really important to you?*

*Did you ever lose or break
something that belonged
to someone else?*

*Was an injustice
ever done to you?*

*Share a favorite
fall memory.*

_____

_____

_____

_____

_____

_____

_____

October 20

*Do you have a story about
standing up against odds for
something you really believed in?*

_____

_____

_____

_____

_____

October 21

*What is the farthest you
ever ran or walked?*

_____

_____

_____

_____

_____

October 22

Did you ever pick apples?

If you had a watch,
tell about it.

*What hobbies or collections
did you have as a youth?*

_____

_____

_____

_____

_____

_____

_____

_____

_____

_____

October 25

*Share a memory about
being very scared.*

_____

_____

_____

_____

_____

_____

_____

_____

_____

October 26

Tell a story about a time when
you dressed up in a costume.

October 27

Did you ever tell ghost stories?

October 28

Do you have a good ghost or
haunted house story to relate?

October 29

What did people
do at Halloween?

October 30

Do you have a special
Halloween memory?

October 31

November questions will deal with your courtship,
marriage, and my arrival in the world.

Tell about how you first knew my father.

_____

_____

_____

_____

_____

November 1

Tell about your first date with him.

_____

_____

_____

_____

_____

November 2

What qualities first attracted you to him?

_____

_____

_____

_____

_____

November 3

*Tell about how my dad
proposed marriage to you.*

*If you have a picture taken
during your courtship to
share, place it here.*

*When and where
were you married?* _____

_____

_____

_____

_____

_____

_____

_____

_____

_____

_____

November 6

What did you wear? _____

_____

_____

_____

_____

_____

_____

_____

_____

_____

November 7

Who performed the ceremony?
Who stood up with you?

November 8

Tell about any other circumstances
of your wedding day.

November 9

Did you go on a honeymoon?

Veteran's Day…
Name the veterans in your family
and times during which they served.

*Tell about where you
lived when first married.* _____

_____

_____

_____

_____

_____

_____

November 12

*What was your
job at the time?* _____

_____

_____

_____

_____

November 13

*What qualities in my dad did you
try unsuccessfully to change?* _____

_____

_____

_____

_____

November 14

Tell about the most serious problem or challenge you faced during your early years of marriage.

_____
_____
_____
_____
_____
_____
_____
_____
_____

November 15

Tell the full names, birthdays, and birthplaces of all of your children.

_____
_____
_____
_____
_____
_____
_____
_____

November 16

*Tell about the
day I was born.*

*How did you
choose my name?*

*What other names did
you consider for me?*

*Many people remember just
what they were doing when they
heard of the assassination of
John F. Kennedy. If you are not
old enough to have that time
etched in your memory, relate
any other childhood story.*

Who was the President
when I was born? _____

_____

_____

_____

_____

_____

November 21

_____

If you have a baby picture of
me to share, place it here. _____

_____

_____

_____

_____

November 22

What was the address of
my first childhood home? _____

_____

_____

_____

_____

November 23

What do you remember most
about my first month of life?

November 24

What were my other
childhood addresses?

November 25

Share your favorite funny
story of me as a child.

_____

_____

_____

_____

_____

_____

_____

_____

November 26

Share a favorite
Thanksgiving memory.

_____

_____

_____

_____

_____

_____

_____

November 27

*Tell about the Thanksgiving
traditions of your youth. What foods
were on your Thanksgiving table?*

_____

_____

_____

_____

_____

November 28

Tell your all-time favorites:

Food- _____

Book- _____

Movie- _____

November 29

More favorites:

TV Show- _____

Song- _____

Color- _____

November 30

More favorites:

Bible verse-

_____

_____

_____

Pastime-

_____

_____

_____

_____

December 1

As a youth, who was your
favorite movie star? Why?

_____

_____

_____

_____

_____

_____

_____

December 2

*Use the next 3 entries for
anything else you would like me
to know about your childhood.*

December 3

December 4

December 5

Do you have any
knowledge of how your
first name was chosen?

December 6

Pearl Harbor Day…
If you are not old enough to relate
a memory of that day, relate any
other childhood remembrance.

December 7

Tell about something you built,
designed, or made as a youth.

December 8

Tell about your favorite
stores to browse in as a child.

What did you like
to look at there?

Were you ever in a church or school
Christmas or Holiday pageant?

December 9

December 10

December 11

*(If the following Christmas topics do not apply, please share
your special Holiday memories and traditions.)*

When did you put up your Christmas tree?
Where did you get them? _____

_____

_____

_____

December 12

How did you decorate your trees? _____

_____

_____

_____

_____

December 13

Did you hang a Christmas stocking? _____

_____

_____

_____

_____

December 14

Did your Grandpa or Grandma ever make gifts for you? Tell about them.

December 15

Tell about the neatest present you remember giving to your mom.

December 16

*Tell about the neatest present you
remember giving to your dad.*

*Tell about the best
Christmas present you
ever received, as a child.*

Tell about the worst Christmas present
you ever received, as a child.

_____

_____

_____

_____

_____

December 19

Tell about your experiences
with Santa Claus.

_____

_____

_____

_____

December 20

Do you remember a "best"
Christmas of childhood?

_____

_____

_____

_____

December 21

Tell about Holiday celebrations at a relative's house during your childhood.

_____
_____
_____
_____
_____
_____
_____

December 22

Did your family observe the birth of Jesus at Christmas? In what ways?

_____
_____
_____
_____
_____
_____

December 23

Tell about the most memorable gifts you have given me.

_____
_____
_____
_____
_____
_____

December 24

*Tell about the most memorable
gifts I have given you.*

_____

_____

_____

_____

_____

_____

_____

_____

_____

December 25

*Share any other
Christmas memory.*

_____

_____

_____

_____

_____

_____

_____

December 26

Is there anything else that you would like me to know about _my_ childhood?

December 27

December 28

Do you remember celebrating any special wedding anniversaries of your parents or grandparents?

December 29

What special memories do you have of New Year's Eve or New Year's Day?

December 30

If you were to make a New Year's Resolution this year, what might it be?

December 31

Memory Journals for Special People

Grandma, Tell Me Your Memories – Heirloom Edition
Grandpa, Tell Me Your Memories – Heirloom Edition
Mom, Share Your Life With Me – Heirloom Edition
Dad, Share Your Life With Me – Heirloom Edition
Grandma, Tell Me Your Memories
Grandpa, Tell Me Your Memories
Mom, Share Your Life With Me
Dad, Share Your Life With Me
To the Best of My Recollection
To My Dear Friend
My Days...My Pictures
My Days...My Writings
My Life...My Thoughts
Sisters
Mom, Tell Me One More Story...Your Story of Raising Me
Dad, Tell Me One More Story...Your Story of Raising Me